Dedication

To my daughter Taylor, my mini-me, who is the inspiration for this book and has driven my ambitions since the moment you came into this world. Mommy will always love you!

Mommy, am I pretty?

In my eyes you are the most beautiful little girl on the planet. It is always better to be smart than pretty, however, so don't take that for granted.

Mommy, am I smart?

In my eyes you are the smartest person there is. You can achieve anything, be anything and pass every quiz.

Mommy, am I a good dancer?

In my eyes you are as hip
as a bunny and smooth as a
snake. You could be the prima
ballerina in Swan Lake.

Mommy, am I a

In my eyes you are better than Leonardo Da Vinci. I'm sure many would agree. Your work will hang in museums for all to see.

good artist?

Mommy, am I funny?

In my eyes you are hilarious. You could be a comic. You're quick to the punch lines and they are always classic.

Mommy, am I kind?

In my eyes you are caring, giving and thoughtful. You are mommy's little angel.

Mommy, am I strong?

In my eyes you are as strong as a screw, but I will always be there to hold and protect you.

Mommy, am I a good girl?

In my eyes you are the best. Though you may get into trouble from time to time, it's to teach you right from wrong and to make sure you are fine.

Mommy, am I a big girl?

In my eyes you are a big girl, and quite the young lady. Never forget, you will always be my baby.

Mommy, I sure am a lot of things,

but in my eyes you are the greatest mommy there is and that is truly a blessing.

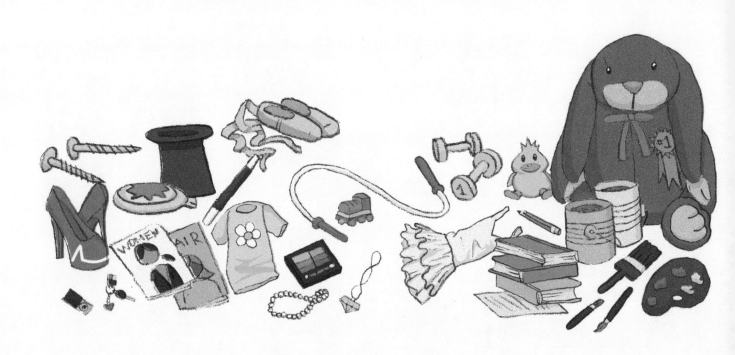

About the Author & Illustrator

Author
Monique Curry

Mommy am I pretty, mommy am I smart? In My Eyes answers questions asked by little girls in a fun and loving way. It affirms that YES you are beautiful, smart and can achieve anything and everything!

Annamarie Lewis is a Graphic Designer who grew up in Long Island, New York. She enjoys drawing, music, and watching movies. She attended Elizabeth City State University.

Illustrator
Annamarie Lewis